Hi there. My guess is, that as you are holding this book in your hand, someone in your life has died.

Every year Winston's Wish work with thousands of young people when someone important to them dies. Of course there's nothing anyone can do to bring that person back, and remembering him or her may always seem a bit painful. But it can also be helpful, even fun, and it is an important part of your life going forward.

Over the next few pages you'll meet some people who've had their own experience of bereavement. They've got some ideas for activities you can do to help you deal with your experience and collect your memories in creative ways. At the back of the book are some templates that you can cut out or photocopy and use to help you.

Have a flick through, see which activities appeal to you and, if you want, alter them to suit you more. The important thing is not the activity – it's finding a way for you to hold on to your memories of the person who died.

By the way, I'm Andy. That's me in the red shirt. You'll be seeing me throughout the book with some useful tips and ideas from people who have already done these activities.

So, be prepared for some laughs, probably some tears, a load of memories, and a lot of glue! Enjoy…

I KNOW HOW YOU FEEL KATE, I FELT THE SAME WHEN MY DAD DIED. BUT IN THIS BOOK YOU'LL FIND LOTS OF WAYS TO HELP YOU REMEMBER.

THERE ARE LOTS OF DATES THAT ARE IMPORTANT TO ME. MOST OF THEM BECAUSE THEY WERE SPECIAL DAYS WITH MY DAD.

I ESPECIALLY LIKE TO REMEMBER HIM ON HIS BIRTHDAY AND AT NEW YEAR, WHEN WE USED TO SET OFF FIREWORKS TOGETHER.

CALENDAR OF MEMORIES

Throughout the year there will be many moments when you remember the person who has died. Some days may seem especially important though. Making a Calendar of Memories could help you on these days, when you might be missing the person who died.

STEP 1 Make a list of some dates which you would like to remember. Think about birthdays, anniversaries, Christmas, New Year, Mother's Day, Father's Day, family events and any other dates that are significant to you.

STEP 2 Using the template at the back of this book note down these important dates. You may also like to think of things you might want to do on these days, for example, on dad's birthday, light a candle and cook his favourite meal.

STEP 3 You may want to simply write the details onto the calendar, or you may wish to make it look more interesting by using photos and pictures...make it exactly how you want it.

STEP 4 Once you have finished it, decide how you are going to display your calendar. You could pin it to the wall, put it in a frame, or stick it to the fridge. Also think about who you might tell about your important dates, they could then support you on these days.

TOOLKIT

Definitely need
- Ideas template (see page 23)
- Pens
- Scissors
- Coloured pens

Optional
- Photos
- Magazines to cut pictures from
- Glue and a display folder or frame

22

> I MADE A REAL EFFORT TO THINK OF DAYS THAT WERE IMPORTANT TO ME, NOT JUST TO OTHER PEOPLE. I ALSO THOUGHT LONG AND HARD ABOUT WHAT I WAS GOING TO DO TO MARK THESE OCCASIONS.

Mum had been going on and on at me about doing my homework ..it was doing my head in. The morning she died I shouted at her and slammed the front door as I left for school. I never saw her alive again. For ages I felt guilty about being so angry towards her. These stones help me balance the difficult, ordinary and special things about Mum.

MEMORY STONES

In every relationship we have, there are often difficult, special and ordinary moments. Ordinary memories you have may be that the person liked 2 sugars in their coffee, or used to always walk you to school. The special memories could be the holidays you went on, watching films together, or buying sweets on a Friday. There will also be some memories that are difficult to think about, these can hurt and feel painful, however they are still important memories. This activity will help you to balance all these difficult, special and ordinary memories.

STEP 1   Find somewhere to keep your stones. You may want to store them in a small bag, box, or you could display them on a shelf.

STEP 2   You will need three stones. One needs to be ordinary, smooth and round, like a pebble. The second needs to be a rough stone with sharp jagged edges. The third needs to be special, like a precious Gemstone. Beaches, garden centres, and craft shops are great places to get cool stones!

STEP 3   Spend time holding each stone. First the ordinary one. Think of some everyday memories you have of the person. Now hold the rough stone. Are there some memories which are hard to think about and feel painful? Maybe there are things that you wish were different? Finally hold the precious stone. Think of the special moments and times that you shared together?

TOOLKIT

Definitely need

- A rough sharp rock
- A smooth ordinary pebble
- A precious shiny gemstone
- Somewhere to keep these stones

MOST RELATIONSHIPS HAVE GOOD TIMES AND BAD TIMES. USE THESE STONES TO REPRESENT ALL YOUR MEMORIES BUT FOCUS ON THE ONES THAT HELP YOU TO FEEL CLOSE TO THE PERSON WHO DIED.

When I think of Charlie, I used to only think of the day he died. This film roll helped me to realize that I had lots of memories from before his death, and lots that have happened since. Charlie dying is not the only thing to ever happen in my life.

TELLING YOUR STORY

When someone important dies, you can sometimes forget about everything else and can only think of that moment. It might often play round and round in your head, popping into your imagination at all sorts of moments. This activity helps you think of before, during and after the event, and helps you to take some control over when you 'view your story'.

STEP 1 Get some coloured pens, pencils, and the film rolls from the back of this book. (You may need to photocopy this sheet a few times). Decide what you might include on this film roll. Think of it as a movie of your life…include all of the important things that have happened to you.

STEP 2 Draw your life scenes on the film roll, showing what your life was like before the person died. Include details such as who was important to you, and what they looked like. Include photos if you want to.

STEP 3 Next, draw how the person you are remembering, died. You may want to include pictures or words. Include as much information as is comfortable, but make sure that you have a full story on your film roll. Finish off with details of the funeral, and then how life is now, who is important to you and what has changed.

STEP 4 Give equal space to each section of your story, don't focus too much on one scene, or ignore another part – a complete story is a good one! You could use this to help tell your story to other people.

TOOLKIT

Definitely need
- Film roll template (see p25)
- Scissors
- Coloured pens/pencils
- Sticky tape

Optional
- Photos
- Glue

NOW YOU HAVE FINISHED TELLING YOUR STORY. YOU CAN CHOOSE WHEN YOU WANT TO WATCH IT. IT DOESN'T NEED TO PLAY CONTINUALLY IN YOUR HEAD ANYMORE; YOU CAN PRESS THE 'EJECT' BUTTON.

mum died when i was only eight years old. now that i am nearly finishing secondary school i cant remember her as clearly as i could then. looking through my memory box reminds me of the good times we used to share.

memory box

In a memory box you can keep and treasure all kinds of things that remind you of the person who has died. You can customise it to make it more personal, and fill it with photos, letters, and objects that remind you of your experiences together.

step 1 Find a box. It can be any type of box – it just has to be big enough for everything you want to keep in it. You could use a shoe box, or a biscuit tin. (Winston's Wish sells specially made memory boxes which you can buy).

step 2 Decorate the box. You could use wrapping paper, pictures cut out of magazines, photos, stickers, shells or paints…be creative!

step 3 Once the box is decorated, start filling it. You can put anything you want in it (as long as it will fit!). Check with other people in your family that it is ok with them for you to have things like photos and objects which belonged to the person who has died. Below are a few ideas of some things that you could include – but don't stop there – there's loads more.

Photos
CD of music they liked
Their perfume
Cards
Letters
Postcards from holidays
Jewellery
Items of clothing
Pictures you drew for them

toolkit

- A box
- Some things to remind you of the person who has died
- Tape
- Glue
- Pens and things to personalise your box

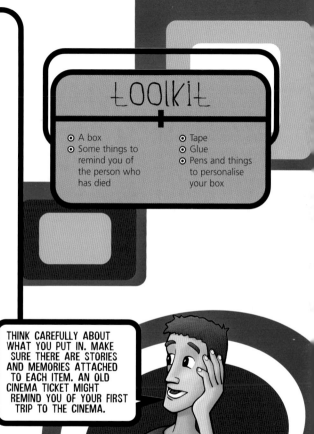

THINK CAREFULLY ABOUT WHAT YOU PUT IN. MAKE SURE THERE ARE STORIES AND MEMORIES ATTACHED TO EACH ITEM. AN OLD CINEMA TICKET MIGHT REMIND YOU OF YOUR FIRST TRIP TO THE CINEMA.

I think about my little brother all the time, sometimes when I am not really expecting to, like when I am in the middle of watching a film. Other times I really want to just sit down and remember him for a while, and focus on nothing else. That's when I light my candle.

lighting a memory candle

There is nothing magical about a candle, but lighting one, sitting down and spending some time thinking of the person who died can be very special. It maybe a little painful, and tears sometimes flow – that's ok. As you spend some time thinking, you may also like to look at photos or objects that belonged to the person who died.

step 1 Find a candle that you like. There are hundreds of different styles available, so shop around. Make sure it can stand up securely (you may need a holder for this).

step 2 Set up a space you can use for a while where you won't be interrupted or disturbed. It could be your bedroom, garden or anywhere else that is private to you.

step 3 Near to the candle, place photos of you and the person you are remembering and maybe some other things that remind you of them. Don't overcrowd it though – you want some space to just think.

step 4 When you are ready, light the candle and simply sit and think of the memories that you want to. You may want to listen to some music, or just sit in silence, it is up to you. After a little while, when you are ready - blow the candle out.

toolkit

Definitely need

⊙ A candle (with permission from an adult in your house to light it)
⊙ Matches or a lighter

Optional

⊙ Photo of the person who died
⊙ Objects that remind you of the person who died
⊙ A piece of music that you like

HAVE SOME TISSUES READY IN CASE YOU NEED THEM.

BE CAREFUL. CANDLES LOOK GREAT BUT CAN BE A FIRE HAZARD.

14

FIRST AID KIT

On difficult days when you may be feeling low, this kit will help you think of ways to be in charge of those feelings, and hopefully, put a little smile on your face. You can fill it with whatever you want, and keep adding to it as you think of more things.

STEP 1 List some things that make you feel a bit better when you are feeling down. You may have a favourite CD, DVD or computer game that cheers you up. Maybe there is a place you like to visit, or a particular food you like to eat. Or, how about a friend who always cheers you up when you text or phone them.

STEP 2 Find something that you could turn into your First Aid Kit. It could be a bag, shoebox, or biscuit tin. Then decorate it, making it personal to you.

STEP 3 Place the items you chose into your First Aid Kit. If some of the items are too big (your friend who you like to phone for instance!) you could make a little model of them or draw a picture of them.

STEP 4 On difficult days use your First Aid Kit. Some things will help you take control of your difficult feelings, others may remind you of good memories of the person who died. Although it is sometimes painful, it can be good to remember them.

TOOLKIT

Definitely need
- Some ideas of things that make you feel better
- A box or a bag

Optional
- Art stuff to decorate the box
- Coloured pens
- Modeling clay
- Glue

THERE ARE SOME REALLY GOOD THINGS THAT MIGHT BE IMPOSSIBLE TO GET INTO THE BOX. BE CREATIVE. USE PICTURES, MODELS, POSTCARDS, PHOTOS AND OBJECTS. LEAVE SPACE TO ADD MORE THINGS.

MEMORY JAR

Each different colour in your Memory Jar will represent a memory that you have of the person that died. Whether happy or sad they are important memories to you. You might think of holidays you used to have at the beach and choose the colour yellow. Or if they were angry a lot you can represent that with the colour red.

STEP 1 Begin by thinking of 5 memories of the person who died that you want to capture in your Memory Jar. Assign a colour to each memory. Colour the Memory Jar template (at the back of this book) with the colours you have chosen, and write the memory next to it. (You may want to frame it now so that it doesn't smudge).

STEP 2 Fill a jar right up to the brim with salt, making sure it is jammed full. This gives you the exact amount of salt needed. Then tip the salt out of the jar into 5 piles. Each of these piles will repesent a memory, so you could make them equal in size, or if you have a more significant memory, put more salt in that pile.

STEP 3 Pick a coloured chalk and start to rub it into the salt of one pile. As you rub it in, the salt will begin to turn that colour. Keep rubbing until it is the colour you want – the longer you rub, the more vibrant the colour!

STEP 4 Once you have coloured all five piles of salt, carefully tip them into the jar. You can do them in straight layers, or diagonal ones, in thin strips or large ones, it is totally up to you. Once you have finished, place a cotton wool ball on top and screw the lid back on.

TOOLKIT

Definitely need
- A Jar (Jam /paste / baby food etc)
- Packet of table salt
- Coloured chalks or pastels
- "My memory jar" template (p27)
- Cotton wool ball

Optional
- Clip frame for your memory jar template

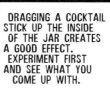

DRAGGING A COCKTAIL STICK UP THE INSIDE OF THE JAR CREATES A GOOD EFFECT. EXPERIMENT FIRST AND SEE WHAT YOU COME UP WITH.

WHEN MUM DIED I WAS VERY YOUNG. SOMETIMES I REALLY STRUGGLE TO REMEMBER HER. THIS LIFE RECORD HAS HELPED ME BUILD A PICTURE OF MY MUM.

LIFE RECORD

Remembering someone who has died is really important, but can sometimes be difficult to do. Memories seem to fade as time passes, and at other times, things you have not thought of for ages suddenly pop into your mind. Putting all of these memories together in one place means they will always be within reach.

STEP 1   Decide what type of record you are going to make. There are lots of different types, and the one that you use depends on you, your skills and personality. Some people like to create a book of photos, poems, pictures and thoughts. Or, you could make a website, short film, time capsule or an album. You may want other people to contribute, or you may want to keep it private.

STEP 2   Think about what you want to include in your record: Information about the childhood of the person who died (you may want to talk to their relatives to find out more). What did they look like? What did they enjoy? What was their favourite meal? Or the piece of clothing that they wore the most? Were they married? What were they proud of? What was their favourite music? What did they get annoyed at? What were they good at? What were they bad at? What is your earliest memory of them? Where did they work? What did you do together?

STEP 3   Once you have decided on what you want to include in your life record...start creating!

TOOLKIT

Only need

⊙ Your imagination

ONCE YOU HAVE MADE YOUR LIFE RECORD OF THE PERSON WHO DIED KEEP IT IN A SAFE PLACE. WHEN IMPORTANT MEMORIES POP INTO YOUR HEAD UNEXPECTEDLY NOTE THEM DOWN AND PUT THEM IN YOUR RECORD.

TOP 10 TIPS

Although you may miss the person who has died at any moment on any day, there are some days when you think of them even more than usual. For instance the day that would have been their birthday, Christmas Day, Father's Day, Mother's Day, Easter, the anniversary of their death or New Year. These are ideas of things you can do on these days. There are loads more – use these to get you started.

Read through the ideas below. Pick ones you like...then do them!

1. Make a special card and take it to their grave, the place where their ashes are, or a place that was special to you.

2. Tie a message or wish to a helium filled balloon and let it soar into the sky.

3. Plant a bulb or a shrub in a place that will allow them to grow and flourish in memory of the person.

4. Cook their favourite meal and eat it.

5. Listen to their favourite music, or some music you remember listening to together.

6. Make, or buy a new photo frame for your favourite picture of them.

7. Write a letter, a poem or song about how you are feeling and what you would want that person to know.

8. At Christmas decorate a special tree bauble and hang it in memory of them.

9. Use your own memory candle to help you think of them for a while.

10. Chat with other family members and all share your favourite memory of the person.

SO THERE YOU HAVE IT. DON'T FORGET TO USE THE TEMPLATES ON THE NEXT FEW PAGES AND IF YOU NEED TO GET IN TOUCH WITH WINSTON'S WISH, ALL OF THEIR DETAILS ARE AT THE FRONT OF THIS BOOK.
AND DON'T FORGET – KEEP REMEMBERING!

HERE ARE SOME OF THE TEMPLATES THAT WE HAVE MENTIONED IN THE BOOK. IF YOU WOULD LIKE SOME IDEAS TO GET YOU STARTED TAKE A LOOK AT THE RELEVANT PAGES

CALENDAR OF MEMORIES

For instructions on how to use this template please refer to page 5 of this booklet.

TREASURE GOOD MEMORIES

especially on important days like these.

TELLING YOUR STORY

For instructions on how to use this template please refer to page 9 of this booklet.

MEMORY JAR

For instructions on how to use this template please refer to page 17 of this booklet.

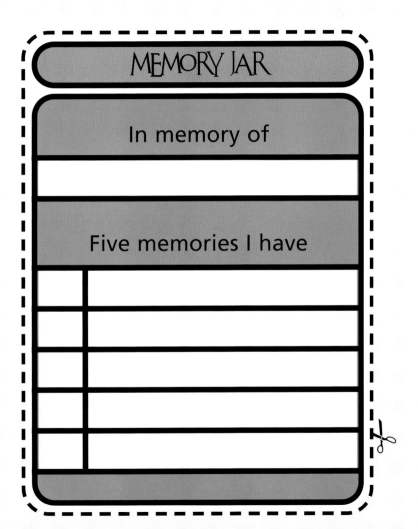

MEMORY JAR

In memory of

Five memories I have